Rare
Wildlife
in
Leicestershire
and Rutland

Publication of this book was made possible by generous support from the sponsors, Rare Ltd, based in Twycross, one of the most prolific and widely respected videogame developers in the world today.

Rare Wildlife

in
Leicestershire
and Rutland

Andrew Heaton

Leicestershire
and Rutland

LEICESTERSHIRE MUSEUMS
ARTS & RECORDS SERVICE

in association with
KAIROS PRESS
1998

ISBN 1 871344 17 4

First edition, 1998

Design and Layout by Robin Stevenson, Kairos Press
Body text in Aldine 721 BT, 11pt.
Imagesetting by Double Vision, Leicester
Printed in Great Britain by Norwood Press, Anstey, Leicester.

British Library Cataloguing in Publication Data.
A CIP catalogue record for this publication
is available from the British Library.

Leicestershire and Rutland Wildlife Trust
1 West Street, Leicester, LE1 6UU

Leicestershire Museums, Arts and Records Service
216 Birstall Road, Birstall, LE4 4DG

in association with

KAIROS PRESS
552 Bradgate Road
Newtown Linford
Leicester LE6 0HB

Contents

Reed warbler

ACKNOWLEDGEMENTS

The production of this book would not have been possible without the efforts of many people over the years who have worked to record and conserve wildlife in Leicester, Leicestershire and Rutland. Particular mention should be made of the authors of the full Red Data Book, as listed on page 9. Michael Jeeves and Jenny Harris, Leicestershire and Rutland Wildlife Trust, and Derek Lott and Darwyn Sumner, Leicestershire Museums, Arts and Records Service, have been especially helpful in providing information and illustrative material. Many useful suggestions, on all aspects of the publication, were made by Robin Stevenson of Kairos Press. Photographs have been provided by Peter Gamble, Peter Jones, Jim Eaton, Bob Stebbings, Leicestershire and Rutland Wildlife Trust and the Environment Agency; thanks are due to them all.

The black and white illustrations have been drawn from a number of sources including Hulme, F E (1906) *Familiar Wild Flowers*; Lydekker, R (ed.) (1896) *The Royal Natural History*; Wood, J G (1889) *Lane and Field*; Wood, J G (c1900) *The Brook and its Banks*.

WHAT IS A RED DATA BOOK?

*R*ed Data Books, an idea first developed by the late Sir Peter Scott, are becoming increasingly important tools in conservation. They help to draw attention to the plight of the rarest and most threatened animals and plants. They also identify the essential conservation measures that need to be taken to ensure the survival of these species. This has become of great significance with the current interest in biodiversity, both nationally and at a local scale – in this case, the local authority areas of Leicestershire, Leicester and Rutland.

Initially, Red Data Books (RDBs) were produced for a particular group of animals or plants at a national scale. Recently, county Red Data Books have been produced to cover all groups of animals and plants found in an area – this present volume is an example of that approach. So far, coverage of the country has been rather patchy, though the East Midlands has been well served; the first county RDB was that for Lincolnshire which appeared in 1988, whilst the Derbyshire RDB was published in 1995, and Northamptonshire's in 1996.

The Red Data Book for Leicestershire, Leicester and Rutland has been compiled over the last few years through the efforts of a large number of people. It has been a joint project between Leicestershire and Rutland Wildlife Trust, Leicestershire County Council Museums, Arts and Records Service and English Nature.

PUTTING TOGETHER THE LEICESTERSHIRE RED DATA BOOK

*T*he Leicestershire RDB differs from the other East Midlands reports in an important respect. Whilst the other counties set out all the information in a single publication, for Leicestershire, Leicester and Rutland, a series of RDB volumes has been produced, each of which contains much detail on the plant or animal group concerned. It is from these "full" RDB reports that the information has been taken to compile this summary. The full volumes that have been published so far are listed on page 9.

In choosing the critical species to be included, each of the RDB reports was produced to a common set of six criteria. These were:

R	Rarity	Species recorded from three or fewer one-kilometre national grid squares since 1960.
E	Endangered species and habitats	Species confined to sites and habitats which are particularly threatened by development or land management practices.
D	Declining species	All species which have significantly declined in numbers to the point where their survival is at risk.
B	Red Data Book species	Those species which are listed in the various national Red Data Books.
N	Nationally Notable species	Species which do not automatically qualify for national RDBs, but which are recognised as being important on a national scale.
P	Legally Protected species	Species which are given legal protection under the Wildlife and Countryside Act 1981 and other legislation. (P) indicates partial protection.

THE FULL RED DATA BOOK

*T*he full Red Data Book for Leicestershire, Leicester and Rutland consists of the volumes listed below. In each of these, all the threatened species in that group are allocated to one of the categories shown opposite, and details of their ecology, threats and conservation needs are given.

Group	Author	Publication date
Vascular Plants	M Jeeves	1993
Coleoptera	D Lott	1995
Birds	M Jeeves	1996
Mammals, Reptiles, Amphibians and Fish	J Dawson and A Heaton	1997
Butterflies and Moths	J McPhail and R Morris	1997
Bryophytes	D Ballard and A Fletcher	1997
Lichens	A Fletcher	In draft
Fungi	Fungus Study Group	In preparation

These volumes are available from Leicestershire and Rutland Wildlife Trust. The information in this book is taken from the full volumes; not every species can be included here, but it gives a flavour of the wide range of wildlife which is under threat locally, and in need of conservation action.

CONSERVING THE RED DATA BOOK SPECIES

*L*ike many Midland counties, Leicestershire and Rutland have lost much of their wildlife to pressures such as development and agricultural intensification. Much remains, of course, especially in certain areas – Rutland Water is a wetland of international importance for its waterfowl populations; Charnwood Forest, with its heathland and woodland, is nationally important for wildlife as well as being of international geological significance. However, there is a need to be ever-vigilant to the threats, and to take positive action to maintain the wildlife populations which we have. This Red Data Book is intended to highlight these threats and actions.

Statutory protection is given to key species, and the sites they inhabit, by the Wildlife and Countryside Act 1981. Around 90 sites (most in Leicestershire, one fifth in Rutland and just one in the city) are given legal protection under this Act by their designation as Sites of Special Scientific Interest (SSSIs). These are the real gems of the countryside: SSSIs are chosen as the best examples of the various habitats – Bradgate Park and Charnwood Lodge for heathlands, the woodlands of Owston and Launde, wetlands such as Narborough Bog and Great Bowden Borrow Pit. SSSI designation gives protection by placing restrictions on landowners' activities, and they are also significant considerations in the planning process.

In addition to the SSSIs, around 1000 Wildlife Sites, important at the county scale, are recognised for Leicestershire, Leicester and Rutland and appear in planning documents. Lacking statutory protection, these may not be the very top sites, but they provide the context for the SSSIs – if they disappear, key species will be under even greater pressure. There is little future for those species marooned on island SSSIs if the surrounding countryside is hostile.

A number of SSSIs and some Wildlife Sites are managed as nature reserves. The Wildlife Trust has by far the greatest number of these – around 40 across the two counties. They range from small local sites such as Our Lady's Well in Oakham to the expanses of Rutland Water. Other nature reserves are run by local authorities – Beacon Hill by Leicestershire

County Council, Burbage Common by Hinckley and Bosworth Borough Council, for example – by English Nature (Muston Meadows National Nature Reserve), or by other voluntary bodies (such as Plantlife's Seaton Meadows). In the City, several sites are managed by Environ, some in collaboration with the Wildlife Trust.

It is important to note that these sites are actively managed by the bodies that run them. It is not true that you can simply put a fence around a site, leave it alone and call it a nature reserve. Reserves need management to maintain the best conditions for their wildlife, which can take up a lot of resources. Neglect – lack of management – has led to a lot of the problems facing animals and plants in the Red Data Book – the scrubbing over of grassland sites, lack of woodland management, and similar. Unfortunately, even in SSSIs, it is not possible to enforce management if landowners are not interested.

The other aspect of the Wildlife and Countryside Act 1981 is the protection given to key individual species, which prevents them and their homes from being disturbed. As well as giving protection to all native birds (with the exception of a few pest species), the Act also provides specific protection for a number of animals and plants. Amongst those found in Leicestershire and Rutland are the otter, water vole, dormouse, the bats, great crested newt and other amphibians and reptiles, and the native crayfish. The European Habitats Directive has recently confirmed the importance of many of these and given protection to a further range of species such as bullhead, brook lamprey and spined loach. All of these species need special consideration in the Leicestershire and Rutland context, and hence they feature in this Red Data Book.

The conservation of wildlife species has again been given a boost in recent years by the signing, by the UK Government, of the Biodiversity Convention at the Rio Earth Summit in 1992. This led directly, at a local level, to the Leicestershire, Leicester and Rutland Biodiversity Action Plan (BAP) which has taken significant work from local conservationists recently. After the preparation of an audit, detailing the wildlife resource of the area, a full biodiversity plan was published in 1998, which identified priorities for conservation and defined goals and objectives. It was set out in the form of action plans for individual species and habitats – 17 habitats and 14 species initially, including species appearing in the Red Data Book such as redstart, black poplar and bats. The publication of the BAP was a joint effort of a large number of different bodies, and it has led to a greatly increased realisation of the need to conserve vulnerable species, and the resources and actions which are required to do this.

As well as the Leicestershire/Rutland BAP, the National Forest has prepared its own BAP, which covers western Leicestershire as well as parts of Derbyshire and Staffordshire, and Charnwood Borough and Leicester City are currently drafting BAPs for their areas of jurisdiction. If the resources can be found to undertake the actions which are identified in each of these, there may be a brighter future for the species that they are targeting. Perhaps some of the animals and plants detailed in this Red Data Book can be removed from future editions as, through biodiversity action, their populations recover to the point where they are no longer rare and threatened.

Common lizard

MAMMALS

Mammals, though including some of our best-loved native animals, are rather rarely seen in the wild. This means, of course, that declines in populations can occur without being noticed. Brown hares and harvest mice, for example, appear to have suffered from modern agricultural practices, whilst both badgers (protected under their own legislation) and hedgehogs suffer from high numbers of road deaths. All these species (together with the shrews, about which we know rather little) need to be kept under scrutiny to ensure that no significant problems are affecting their populations.

Water shrews

However, it is upon six individual species and one group (the bats) that the Red Data Book concentrates – the rarest and most threatened in Leicestershire and Rutland. Three of these are rodents. The **yellow-necked mouse**, near to the northern edge of its British distribution, has rarely been recorded in the two counties. It is a creature of ancient woodland, so its most recent record, of one trapped in a house in Oakham, is unusual. In a county so lacking in woodland, the hopes of a return of this species appear slim, though it is possible that nestboxes provided for another rarity, the **dormouse**, may help by providing artificial wintering sites.

Dormice require open mixed broadleaved woodland with a rich understorey providing aerial pathways around the wood and a variety of food, notably hazelnuts. With the early loss of ancient woodland in

Leicestershire, dormice were probably never common, and in recent decades there have been only occasional records from woods at Owston, Launde and Pickworth. At the last site, dormouse nest boxes have been erected and monitored, resulting in several positive sightings which indicate at least one breeding population in the county. Further surveys along these lines may detect others, but where they are apparently absent, the reinstatement of appropriate management of woods by coppicing may allow successful reintroductions of dormice from elsewhere.

With populations declining enormously in recent years, the **water vole** may be the most threatened British mammal. A survey in 1994/95 recorded only 12 positive sightings of water voles in Leicester and a further 17 in the rest of the county, with an almost complete absence from major rivers and canals. Only at one site, an aquatic garden centre on the edge of Ashby de la Zouch with a series of ponds, was there a thriving population. Factors such as pollution, excessive river management and cultivation right up to the riverbank have affected water voles, and the last straw has been the spread of American mink which prey upon them very effectively. Control of mink is difficult, though it may be possible on a local scale; the restoration of wetland habitats alongside rivers may be a more effective way of looking after the water vole.

The two carnivores in the Red Data Book are doing rather better than the rodents. **Otters**, which disappeared from the Midlands in the 1960s due to pollution of watercourses by toxic agricultural chemicals, have been moving back from their Welsh stronghold and from introduced populations in East Anglia. There have been several Leicestershire sightings in recent years, including a dead cub in the Ashby Canal in 1993 and a road death on the A1 near Stretton in 1994. Captive-bred otters have also been released into the Rivers Gwash and Welland in Rutland, and are now believed to have bred. The construction of artificial holts, to compensate for lack of natural resting and breeding sites, may help to restore the population.

Otter

Polecat

Equally spectacularly, **polecats** have spread back across the Midlands from Wales in recent years, and the first Leicestershire record for 100 years was, ironically, run over on the A5 near Wibtoft in 1994. Polecats are very adaptable animals and, providing they are not persecuted by misguided landowners, they should be able to recolonise the county.

Roe deer are real rarities in Leicestershire, there having been only four recent records of them, in the woodlands of the Skeffington Valley. Further information is obviously needed on them, and landowners persuaded to fence new woodlands adequately, rather than carrying out deer culls.

Bats generally have suffered enormously from loss of breeding and hibernation sites, particularly ancient woodland, from toxic timber treatment of buildings that they use, and from the intensification of agriculture leading to declines in their insect prey. Ten bat species are present in Leicestershire. Even for the most numerous, the **pipistrelle**, only 200 nursery roosts have been identified, and numbers have remained much the same in recent years. **Brown long-eared bats**, the second commonest species, are known from 100 breeding sites; their low, slow hunting flight makes them vulnerable to domestic cats.

Records of the **noctule** and **Daubenton's bats**, both species regularly found near open water, are widespread in the county, but only very few nursery roosts are known. It is a similar situation for the **whiskered** (a woodland edge species) and **natterer's bats** (found in buildings, notably several parish churches).

Daubenton's bat

Four species of bats are rare in Leicestershire as well as nationally. **Brandt's bat** may be overlooked through confusion with the whiskered; there is only one record, a male found dying at Frog Island, Leicester, in 1987. The most recent **barbastelles** seen were two roosting in a stable block at Barnsdale in 1986; the stables have now been converted into timeshare dwellings. There have been a few records of **Leisler's bat**, including 25 females at a nursery roost at Woodhouse Eaves, which they later vacated.

Most surprisingly, there are two records of the **greater horseshoe bat**, a species generally confined to south-west England. One was in disused mine workings in the north-east of the county, and the other at a derelict underground site in the north-west – this bat had been ringed in the Forest of Dean. For all of the bat species, known haunts need to be strictly protected, with grilles placed on underground hibernation sites where appropriate. The erection of bat boxes will also help. Changes in agricultural practices may be needed to restore good feeding areas for bats.

Red Data Book Mammals

	R	E	D	B	N	P
	Rarity	Endangered	Declining	Red Data Book	Nationally Notable	Legally Protected
Greater Horse-shoe Bat	R	E	D	B	N	P
Whiskered Bat			D?	B		P
Brandt's Bat	R		D?	B		P
Natterer's Bat			D?	B		P
Daubenton's Bat			D?	B		P
Leisler's Bat	R		D?	B		P
Noctule			D	B		P
Pipistrelle			D?	B		P
Barbastelle	R		D?	B	N	P
Brown Long-eared Bat			D	B		P
Polecat	R			B		(P)
Otter				B		P
Roe Deer	R					
Dormouse	R		D	B		P
Yellow-necked Mouse	R			B		
Water Vole			D	B		(P)

Field voles

BIRDS

*B*irds are amongst the most conspicuous and popular forms of wildlife, and have been well studied over the years, so that a lot is known about their distribution and status in Leicestershire and Rutland. Yet, despite the great public interest in birds, they have faced just as many threats in recent decades as other groups of animals and plants. Of a total of 300 bird species recorded, 78 are included in the local Red Data Book, either because they are rare in the counties, or because they occur in winter in nationally or internationally significant numbers.

Around half of the species in the Red Data Book are water birds. The **little grebe**, for example, has been found in winter in nationally important numbers on the River Soar through Leicester and at Rutland Water, and the latter site, together with Eye Brook Reservoir, has national counts of wintering **great crested grebes**. The grebes have benefited from the development of reservoirs and gravel pits in the county; red-necked, **Slavonian** and **black-necked grebes** overwinter in much smaller numbers, and the last of these has bred at two sites in recent years, though disturbance from recreational activities may be a problem.

Of the wildfowl, **shelduck, gadwall, teal, shoveler, pochard** and **tufted duck** all breed regularly in small numbers. Nationally important numbers of wintering pochard, tufted duck, **goldeneye** and **mute swan** occur in

Kingfisher

the counties, whilst shoveler and especially gadwall appear in internationally notable numbers. The gadwall figures (up to 2000, many times the level of international significance) make Rutland Water the most important wintering site in north-west Europe. In contrast, small numbers of **scaup, long-tailed duck** and **smew** appear on the counties' open waters in winter, again especially at Rutland Water, with the threat there of disturbance from recreational activities.

A number of waders appear in the county as rare breeding species. **Oystercatcher** and **ringed plover** are the most uncommon, with only one or two pairs attempting to breed each year; **snipe, curlew** and **redshank** may reach 10 pairs, though their presence continues to be threatened by the drainage of wet grassland. **Little ringed plovers** are faring rather better, numbers of pairs having increased to at least 15, and it is ironic that, if they face problems at all, it is the cessation of working at quarry sites. Most intriguing of all, **avocets** attempted to breed at Rutland Water in 1996.

Twenty to thirty breeding male **woodcock** may be present in any one year, threats to their sites being lack of woodland management and disturbance, though numbers of wintering birds are rather higher. Two waders – **jack snipe** and **green sandpiper** – are included in the Red Data Book because they occur in only small numbers in winter. In contrast, **golden plover**

Grey heron

may be found wintering in internationally significant numbers across the counties. The loss of permanent grasslands, their preferred feeding habitat in winter, may be a concern for this species.

Of the other water birds included in the Red Data Book, the **coot** may be a surprise addition, but both Rutland Water and Stanford Reservoir hold winter populations of national significance; Rutland Water is the second most important site in Britain. Conversely, the **great northern diver** is a rare winter vagrant. The **water rail** is not only a rare wintering species, but also a rare breeder, with less than 10 pairs annually. **Black-headed gulls** and **common terns** are both colonially nesting species, primarily at gravel pits, and are thus particularly vulnerable to disturbance; the most recent gull breeding site has now been flooded.

Coot

The main threats to birds of prey are disturbance, direct persecution and egg collecting. The **buzzard** became extinct in Leicestershire in the nineteenth century, killed as "vermin" by gamekeepers. It was only in the early 1990s that it reappeared as a breeding species in the Belvoir area; provided they are accepted by landowners this time, and good populations of the main prey (rabbits) survive, buzzards should be able to recolonise other suitable areas of the counties. There have been recent reports of breeding in south and east Leicestershire.

Moorhen

Two other breeding species are given special legal protection – the **hobby**, which has seen a recent increase in numbers, possibly to over 20 pairs, and the **peregrine falcon**, which bred for the first time in Leicestershire in 1994, at a site where the birds are vulnerable to disturbance – special efforts will be needed to safeguard the nests. Interestingly, there are suggestions that **goshawks** may now be breeding, and sightings of several **red kites** raises hopes that they may also return to nest.

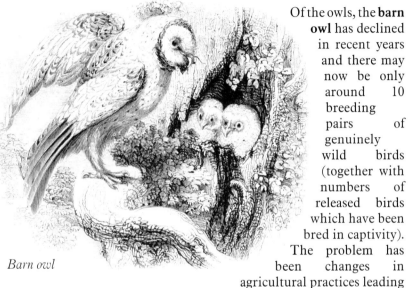

Barn owl

Of the owls, the **barn owl** has declined in recent years and there may now be only around 10 breeding pairs of genuinely wild birds (together with numbers of released birds which have been bred in captivity). The problem has been changes in agricultural practices leading to lower numbers of small mammals and fewer hedgerows. The other two owls mentioned, the **long-eared** and **short-eared owls**, both winter in the county in small numbers, and there are positive records that long-eared owls have nested in recent years.

Despite its importance as a game species, wild populations of **grey partridge** have declined drastically in recent decades as a result of the intensification of agriculture, and there may be few more than 200 pairs in the county now. Changes in agricultural practices, notably early mowing of grass, have also affected the **quail** (together with shooting on migration) so that very few pairs now breed. **Nightjar** numbers have also fallen, with the last proven record of breeding in Rutland in 1974. Here the problem is the loss of its favoured heathland habitat and the maturing of conifer plantations, which nightjars can use for nesting only in their early stages. **Sand martins**, vulnerable because they are a colonial nesting species, occur at two or three regular nesting sites each year, with occasional appearances at others, but the continued working of quarries where there are active colonies remains a threat.

A number of songbirds appear in the Red Data Book as rare breeding species. Several have declined as a result of neglect or inappropriate management of their preferred woodland habitat, notably the **nightingale**, once widespread but now confined to around 10 nesting pairs in Rutland, and the **tree pipit**, both these species suffering from the lack of coppice management. **Redstarts**, birds of open woodland and parkland, have suffered from both the neglect of some woods and the felling and replanting of others, so that their only regular breeding site is the Chater Valley at Launde. Swithland Wood has the only regular haunt of **wood warblers**, where they suffer as ground nesting birds from disturbance by people and dogs. The elusive **hawfinch** also nests in small numbers in the counties, and the **pied flycatcher** is a new breeding species.

The **black redstart** has nested infrequently, but may be overlooked at its preferred sites of power stations and derelict buildings. The **grey wagtail** now breeds annually in the counties, but at few sites; this may not be surprising as it is largely a bird of northern and western Britain, though it has extended eastwards in recent years. Six songbirds appear in the Red Data Book because they overwinter in the county in small numbers. These are the black redstart, **stonechat, blackcap, chiffchaff, common crossbill** and hawfinch.

For a mixed group of farmland birds, it is agricultural intensification and changes in land use practices that have brought about a sharp decline in populations. This has led to the **whinchat** and **wheatear** failing to breed in recent years, though the former turned up again at an opencast site near Ibstock. It has also meant sharp drops in numbers of breeding pairs of such species as **lapwing, turtle dove, skylark, tree sparrow, linnet** and **corn bunting**, and even such apparently common birds as **song thrush, bullfinch, goldfinch** and **swallow**. It is clear that only significant moves to make farming more environmentally sensitive will restore the fortunes of these species.

Goldfinch

Whinchats

Red Data Book Birds : KEY

	B	Rare breeding bird
Rarity	**W**	Rare wintering bird
	BW	Rare both when breeding and over winter
Red Data	**R**	On the "Birds of Conservation Concern **Red** List"
Book	**A**	On the "Birds of Conservation Concern **Amber** List"
Nationally	**WN**	Wintering in nationally important numbers
Notable	**WInt**	Wintering in internationally important numbers
Legally Protected	**P**	Given special protection under Schedule 1 of the Wildlife and Countryside Act 1981 (all birds are given general protection by that Act)

Red Data Book Birds

	R	E	D	B	N	P
	Rarity	Endangered	Declining	Red Data Book	Nationally Notable	Legally Protected
Great Northern Diver	W					P
Little Grebe				A	WN	
Great Crested Grebe					WN	
Red-necked Grebe	W					
Slavonian Grebe	W					P
Black-necked Grebe	B			A		P
Cormorant	B					
Mute Swan					WN	
Shelduck	B					
Gadwall	B				WInt	
Teal	B					
Garganey	B			A		P
Shoveler	B				WInt	
Pochard				A	WN	
Tufted Duck					WN	
Scaup	W					P
Long-tailed Duck	W					P
Goldeneye					WN	
Smew	W					
Buzzard	B					
Kestrel				A		
Hobby	B					P
Peregrine	BW			A		P
Grey Partridge				R		
Quail	B			R		P
Water Rail	BW					
Coot					WN	
Oystercatcher	B					
Little Ringed Plover	B					P
Ringed Plover	B					
Golden Plover					WInt	
Lapwing				A		
Jack Snipe	W					
Snipe	B					
Woodcock	B					
Curlew	B					
Redshank	B					
Green Sandpiper	W					P
Black-headed Gull	B					

Red Data Book Birds (cont.)

	R Rarity	E Endangered	D Declining	B Red Data Book	N Nationally Notable	P Legally Protected
Common Tern	B					
Stock Dove				A		
Turtle Dove				R		
Barn Owl	B			A		P
Long-eared Owl	BW					
Short-eared Owl	W					
Kingfisher				A		P
Green Woodpecker				A		
Skylark				R		
Nightjar	B			R		
Sand Martin	B					
Swallow				A		
Tree Pipit	B					
Grey Wagtail	BW					
Dunnock				A		
Nightingale	B					
Black Redstart	BW			A		P
Redstart	B					
Whinchat	B					
Stonechat	W					
Wheatear	B					
Blackbird				A		
Song Thrush				R		
Blackcap	W					
Grasshopper Warbler				A		
Wood Warbler	B					
Chiffchaff	W					
Spotted Flycatcher				R		
Marsh Tit				A		
Willow Tit				A		
Starling				A		
Tree Sparrow				R		
Goldfinch				A		
Linnet				R		
Common Crossbill	BW					P
Bullfinch				R		
Hawfinch	BW					
Reed Bunting				R		
Corn Bunting				R		

AMPHIBIANS AND REPTILES

With a limited total number of British species and the real rarities (natterjack toad, sand lizard, smooth snake) lacking from the counties, Leicestershire and Rutland support only five species of amphibians and four reptiles. Nevertheless, given the extreme pressures upon the habitats which they favour, primarily wetlands and heathlands respectively, this means that a high proportion of the Leicestershire herpetofauna is of sufficient conservation concern to be detailed in the Red Data Book.

Only the common frog, common toad, smooth newt and grass snake are sufficiently widespread within appropriate habitats to be seen as secure in the counties. Frogs and smooth newts are both able to colonise garden ponds successfully. Toads prefer larger areas of water and are less quick to colonise new sites, but there are significant populations across Leicestershire, and toad patrols have been set up to protect them on their migration back to breeding sites at Coleorton and Ashby Magna. Grass snakes also favour wetland habitats and may be seen regularly, for example, along the canals.

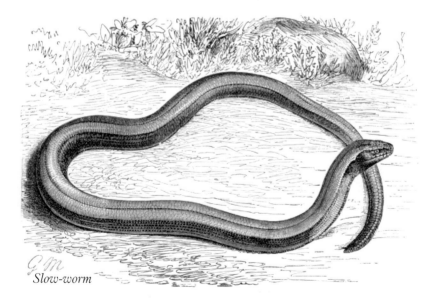

Slow-worm

Great crested newts

Of the five less common species, the **great crested newt** is still widespread but thinly distributed and declining sharply in the East Midlands. The **palmate newt** is at the edge of its range in Leicestershire, being largely absent from eastern England. The three reptiles are all now relatively rare in the Midlands generally, as a result of habitat loss, and recent declines of the **slow-worm** and **adder** in the East Midlands have been significantly greater than across the country as a whole.

The palmate newt is essentially a north-western, upland species, breeding in smaller soft-water ponds, most frequently in heathland/moorland or woodland, often with flowing water close by. Given these habitat requirements, it is not surprising that, in Leicestershire, palmate newts are largely restricted to Charnwood Forest, with the most recent records only from Beacon Hill and, perhaps surprisingly, Knighton. Palmate newts have suffered from both loss of ponds and terrestrial habitat, and the few sites remaining in Leicestershire require appropriate management to prevent overshading. Reintroduction to suitable ponds in Charnwood may be possible.

Great crested newts, a species given full legal protection under the Wildlife and Countryside Act 1981, have also suffered from the great loss of ponds in the county, to urban development, tipping, infilling, drainage and natural succession to drier habitats. They prefer fairly large ponds with a good growth of water plants, together with adequate terrestrial habitat (rough grassland and scrub) and they tend to be fairly faithful to their place of origin. Given the losses of ponds in the county, it is not surprising that great crested newts, although still widely distributed across Leicestershire and Rutland, are nowhere common and are declining significantly. Existing sites for great crested newts need to be managed appropriately, whilst creation of new ponds close to existing sites may establish new breeding populations.

Amongst the reptiles, slow-worms, generally found in drier habitats, have declined sharply in the East Midlands, a decline reflected in Leicestershire populations, especially in the former strongholds of Charnwood and North-West Leicestershire; most recent records have come from Rutland, but these are few. The causes appear to be agricultural intensification and urban development.

Common lizards have suffered similar threats, as well as the afforestation of the heathland that they particularly prefer. Recent records have come only from Rutland and Charnwood Forest. Appropriate management of existing habitats is essential, and heathland restoration may provide opportunities to increase populations.

Although now given protection under the Wildlife and Countryside Act, the adder has suffered direct persecution as well as the loss of its favoured heathland and open woodland habitats. Those few sites where they still occur, mainly in Rutland, require active management to prevent scrub encroachment, and again heathland restoration offers the opportunity of increasing populations.

Adder

Red Data Book Amphibians and Reptiles

	R Rarity	E Endangered	D Declining	B Red Data Book	N Nationally Notable	P Legally Protected
Palmate Newt	R					(P)
Great Crested Newt			D?			P
Slow-worm			D			(P)
Common Lizard	R					(P)
Adder	R	E				(P)

FISH

*D*espite their importance for large numbers of anglers, fish have always been rather neglected by conservationists. Of the 42 native species of British freshwater fish, 25 are or have been found in Leicestershire and Rutland, most being well distributed, though some – silver bream, bleak, ten-spined stickleback, grayling and barbel – are rather localised in the counties' rivers. Two fish species appear in the Red Data Book as being rare and of particular concern in Leicestershire, the **brook lamprey** and the **spined loach**.

Ten-spined sticklebacks

Brook lamprey larvae live in burrows in silt beds, usually in running water, where they filter-feed upon algae. After five to six years, they metamorphose into the adult form. At spawning time, the adults, which do not feed, migrate upstream until they reach suitable spawning grounds, areas of small stones and gravels where the current is not too strong. When the larvae hatch, they drift downstream to find a suitable silt bed. Brook lampreys are rarely recorded in Leicestershire, but spawning has been observed in the River Lin at the Lea Meadows Nature Reserve.

Spined loaches inhabit slow-flowing rivers, canals and ditches, preferring those where there is a good growth of weed, to which their eggs are attached. The species is nocturnal, during daytime remaining half-buried on the bottom in fine sand or mud, and feeds on bottom-dwelling small crustaceans, insect larvae and worms. The spined loach is very uncommon in the Midlands; of the Leicestershire watercourses, it is recorded from the Rivers Mease and Devon and the Grantham Canal.

The Red Data Book includes two fish which are still widespread in Leicestershire and Rutland, but are significant for different reasons. The strange-looking **bullhead** is most commonly to be found in fast-flowing streams and rivers: it is widely distributed in the upper Welland, Chater, Gwash and in Charnwood. Its importance is that the UK

Bullhead

has special responsibility for this species, which though common here, is threatened on the continent. **Brown trout** are also widespread in the better-quality rivers, but many populations have been stocked from farmed fish. Native brown trout are probably only to be found in the Charnwood streams and Soar Brook, where they require conservation measures to preserve their genetic integrity.

Two notable species of fish have become extinct in Leicestershire. Prior to this century, the salmon was common in the Trent and one of the main areas where it was caught was the Kings Mills to Shardlow stretch where the river forms the Leicestershire boundary. Indeed, in the 1880s, the gravels above Kings Mills weir were said to be the main spawning grounds, together with the River Dove. Pollution and the building of structures for industrial and navigation purposes means that there is no longer a run of salmon in the Trent. There is a project to reintroduce them, but the Kings Mills gravels are now unsuitable as spawning areas due to poor water quality.

The burbot, the only freshwater member of the cod family, was once common in many rivers of eastern England, including the Trent and Welland. A combination of factors, including pollution, river management and over-exploitation, meant that by the early 1970s the burbot was extinct in Britain. The last Leicestershire record is not known but judging by the species' history in the Trent catchment generally, it may well have disappeared from the county by the beginning of this century. Consideration is being given to a reintroduction to Britain from continental stock.

Fish populations can be affected by many factors, such as pollution, river management for flood defence and navigation and introductions of fish for sporting purposes (for example, the zander, a fierce non-native predator, is now found in the Ashby Canal). Steps are being taken to tackle some of these threats: there are moves to improve the water quality of rivers, and river management work is generally carried out in a more environmentally-sensitive way these days. Nevertheless, there is a great need to be vigilant, as the case of the burbot shows – fish, being largely unseen and unregarded, can decline and disappear before anyone is aware of the problem.

Red Data Book Fish

	R Rarity	E Endangered	D Declining	B Red Data Book	N Nationally Notable	P Legally Protected
Brown Trout			D?			
Brook Lamprey	R					P
Spined Loach	R					P
Bullhead						P

Bob Stebbings

Above: Noctule – one of the larger bats, widespread but not common.
Below: Water Vole – a species which has been in rapid decline.

Peter Gamble

Above: Gadwall – Rutland Water is the most important wintering site in north-west Europe.
Below: Water Rail – rare both in winter and as a breeding species.

Andrew Heaton

Peter Jones

Peter Jones

Top: Coot – nationally important numbers overwinter at Rutland Water and Stanford Reservoir.

Middle: Swallow – numbers of breeding birds have declined in recent years.

Bottom: Adder – now found at very few sites, mainly in Rutland.

Environment Agency

Environment Agency

Peter Gamble

Above: Marbled White – an attractive butterfly usually found on limestone grassland.

Right: Musk Beetle – dependent upon willow trees and showing a dramatic decline recently.

Opposite –
Top: Great Crested Newt – widespread but nowhere common, a species of European significance.

Middle: Bullhead – found in clean, fast-flowing streams; another species of European concern.

Bottom: Mere Wainscot – one of several wainscot moths associated with wetland habitats.

Peter Gamble

Top: Green Tiger Beetle – a predatory species of open heathland.

Environment Agency

Middle: Whiteclawed Crayfish – survival of this species is threatened by introductions of alien crayfish.

Peter Gamble

Bottom: Variable Blue Damselfly – only positively recorded from three sites.

Peter Gamble

Peter Gamble

Above: Ruddy Darter – this dragonfly is spreading by colonising new ponds.

Left: Black Poplar – one of Britain's rarest tree species.

Peter Gamble

Above: Pasque Flower – an attractive plant of just one limestone grassland site in Rutland.
Below: Petty Whin – a heathland plant found in the Charnwood Forest area.

Peter Gamble

Peter Gamble

Peter Gamble

*Above:
Goldenrod –
found at only
four sites in
recent years.*

*Left: Floating
Water-Plantain
– found only at
Beacon Hill,
this is a species
of European
concern.*

Peter Gamble

Marsh Helleborine – one of several orchids under threat.

Peter Gamble

Above: Lemon-Scented Fern (with hard fern, centre) – restricted to several SSSIs in the north-west of Leicestershire.
Below: Rock Tripe – an uncommon lichen which grows on rocks in Charnwood.

Peter Gamble

River Lin – the Charnwood rivers support critical species such as bullhead and whiteclawed crayfish.

Leicestershire and Rutland Wildlife Trust

Above: Rutland Water – a water supply reservoir which holds wintering birds in huge numbers.
Below: Charnwood Lodge – one of the finest examples of heathland in the Midlands, with species such as petty whin and lesser skullcap.

Leicestershire and Rutland Wildlife Trust

Andrew Heaton

Peter Gamble

Above: Buddon Wood – home to many rare woodland species, this site has largely been lost to quarrying.
Opposite: River Eye – east of Melton Mowbray, this SSSI has populations of whitelegged damselfly and whiteclawed crayfish.
Below: Ketton Quarry – one of the best examples of limestone grassland remaining, with yellow-wort and carline thistle.

Jim Eaton

Peter Gamble

Above: Bradgate Park – ancient parkland trees support many rare beetles.
Below: Narborough Bog – one of several wetlands in the Soar valley, with rare
moths and beetles.

Leicestershire and Rutland Wildlife Trust

BUTTERFLIES AND MOTHS

Several butterflies of conservation concern have been recorded in Leicestershire, including the white admiral, rather uncommon in the East Midlands, and the brown hairstreak and white-letter hairstreak, both of which have declined nationally, through the loss of hedgerows and elms upon which they respectively depend.

However, the Red Data Book concentrates upon four other butterflies as the main conservation priorities in Leicestershire and Rutland. Of most concern is the **black hairstreak**, a national Red Data Book species with a very limited distribution, confined to the East Midlands forest belt. It has only been recorded at a few small, though thriving, colonies, mainly in Rutland. The maintenance of traditional woodland management, allowing the retention of blackthorn scrub which the caterpillars need, is essential if these colonies are to survive.

The **brown argus** has been found at a small number of sites, again in Rutland on limestone areas, notably at Ketton Quarry. It is vulnerable to loss of suitable foodplants – rock-rose, dove's-foot cranesbill and common stork's-bill – because of scrubbing-over of its preferred grassland habitat.

The **marbled white** requires similar conditions to the brown argus, usually being associated with lime-rich grassland. It is again found at Ketton Quarry, and one other site, where the threat of scrub invasion is also a problem (though, unlike the brown argus, the marbled white can tolerate some lack of grazing and rank growth of the grassland).

Nationally widespread but on the edge of its range in Leicestershire, the **dark green**

Meadow brown and Peacock butterflies

fritillary prefers coastal or lime-rich habitats; the handful of records come from a varied selection of sites – a quarry, a wood and a marsh – but there are probably no established breeding colonies.

Amongst the moths, the "micromoths" are the most numerous, but due to lack of information, they have not been fully assessed for the Red Data Book. It appears that four nationally scarce species have been found in Leicestershire, but records still need verification. Of the larger moths, one species, the **concolorous moth**, appears in the national Red Data Book as a rare species. Normally it is regarded as a fenland dweller but, apart from a few records of vagrants, it is to be found at Luffenham Heath in Rutland, an unexpected habitat – this obviously needs further investigation.

A number of truly wetland moths are of conservation concern in the county, notably the wainscots. A close relative of the concolorous, the **mere wainscot**, a moth of marshes and damp woodlands, has suffered habitat loss due to drainage, so that it is now confined to a small number of SSSIs. The **twin-spotted wainscot** is a reedbed species, and much of its stronghold at Burley was drowned by the development of Rutland Water; however, a vigorous colony now exists in the new reedbeds of Rutland Water nature reserve. Both the **brown-veined** and **southern wainscots**, recently found only at Narborough Bog, are threatened by the drying-out of the reedbed and marshy grassland there (so that works have recently been undertaken to bring in more water).

Another Narborough Bog species facing the same threat of desiccation is the **round-winged muslin**, whose caterpillars feed on lichens and mosses. The **small rufous** lives on jointed and soft rush, and is found only at the unusual wetland habitat of Great Bowden Borrowpit reserve. The **hornet moth** and the **pale-lemon sallow** have each been recorded only once in Leicestershire – perhaps not surprisingly, as both species depend upon black poplar trees in floodplain woodlands, and black poplars are now very rare in the county.

The **striped wainscot** inhabits marshes and wet heathland, both very vulnerable habitats, and has not been seen in the county since 1983. A number of moths are linked to heathland, which was once fairly widespread, especially in Charnwood, but has been lost to destruction and lack of management. Species such as the **neglected rustic, small grass emerald, small autumnal** and **ling pug**, feeding largely on heather, have suffered because of this. **Annulet** larvae feed on rock-rose, salad burnet

Left: Hornet moth; centre and right: Goat moth

and bird's foot trefoil as well as heather, and here the loss of low heath grassland to scrub encroachment has been the problem. The restoration of areas of heathland, proposed for Charnwood, would also help restore the fortunes of these species.

Several moths are associated with lime-rich grassland, taking advantage of the variety of plants which grow there. The **small purple-barred**, with a larval food-plant of milkwort, has only been recorded once, at Ketton Quarry, a site which also supports the **six-belted clearwing** at the northern edge of its range in Rutland, feeding on bird's foot trefoil and kidney vetch, and the **bordered sallow**, which requires common or spiny restharrow. Given their requirements for limestone geology, it is not surprising that these species are largely confined to sites in Rutland, with just a few in west Leicestershire. They are vulnerable to agricultural "improvement", or neglect leading to scrubbing-over of the grassland. Moths of neutral grassland include the **grass rivulet**, widespread in Britain but with few Leicestershire records; it feeds on yellow rattle in hay meadows, and has suffered from loss of the habitat, as well as requiring just the right management – an early hay cut may not allow the larvae to develop.

Of the woodland moths, the **yellow-legged clearwing** and **brindled white-spot** are similar in being found in oak woodlands and requiring active management, the clearwing in particular being associated with oak stumps. Another oak species, the **frosted green**, requires more mature trees. The **August thorn** lives on a range of tree species but has been in serious decline throughout England and is on the verge of disappearing from Leicestershire. In some moths, the caterpillars feed not on the trees themselves, but on other woodland plants: the **square-spotted clay**, a very local species, needs burdocks, wood sage or willowherb, and so is found in woods where open rides are maintained; the **four-dotted footman** feeds on various algae and lichens. Amongst moths of wetter woodland, the **northern drab** has been found in old osier beds near Quorn, whilst the **scalloped shell**, present in the Cloud Wood nature reserve, feeds not only on sallow and aspen but also bilberry, and may spread onto the Charnwood heaths if that plant is encouraged.

  The loss of elms, especially in hedgerows, has led to a serious decline in the **white-spotted pinion**, a moth which is rare in the Midlands anyway (and a possible candidate for the national Red Data Book); it has been recorded in only two areas in the counties, but could benefit if elms regenerate. Loss of hedges is a problem for the **maple prominent**, whose larvae feed on field maple, often a hedgerow tree, as well as sycamore. Another hedgerow inhabitant is the **small waved umber**, which lives on traveller's joy growing in lime-rich areas; there is only one county record, at Luffenham Heath.

A small group of uncommon moths is dependent upon artificial habitats. The **wormwood moth** feeds on the wormwood plant, and also on mugwort which is common on wasteland sites; Leicestershire records have come from Leicester gardens and Wanlip gravel pits. The **scarce tissue** feeds on barberry and cultivated varieties of *Berberis*, but its only county site is a garden in Kirby Muxloe where the larvae are found on an Oregon grape plant. It is possible that surveys would show the scarce tissue to be present elsewhere where barberry occurs. The **red-belted clearwing** is found on mature apple trees in orchards and gardens; Leicestershire records are from suburban gardens in the 1970s, and it is possible that the loss of old orchards and increased use of pesticides for fruit spraying may have adversely affected this moth.

Red Data Book Butterflies

	R Rarity	E Endangered	D Declining	B Red Data Book	N Nationally Notable	P Legally Protected
Black Hairstreak	R			B		P
Brown Argus	R					
Dark Green Fritillary	R					
Marbled White	R					

Red Data Book Moths

	R	E	D	B	N	P
	Rarity	Endangered	Declining	Red Data Book	Nationally Notable	Legally Protected
Goat Moth	R				N	
Forester		E			N	
Hornet Moth	R				N	
Currant Clearwing	R				N	
Yellow-legged Clearwing	R				N	
Red-belted Clearwing		E			N	
Large Red-belted Clearwing	R				N	
Six-belted Clearwing					N	
Poplar Lutestring	R					
Frosted Green	R					
Small Grass Emerald	R	E			N	
Birch Mocha	R					
Least Carpet	R				N	
Dotted Border Wave	R	E			N	
Dwarf Cream Wave	R					
Treble Brown Spot	?					
Red Carpet	R	E				
Chalk Carpet	R				N	
Lead Belle	R	E				
Ruddy Carpet	R				N	
Galium Carpet	R					
Small Waved Umber	R					
Fern	R					
Scarce Tissue	R					
Scalloped Shell	R					
Small Autumnal	R	E				
Haworth's Pug	R					
Pinion-spotted Pug					N	
Valerian Pug	R				N	
Netted Pug	R					
Satyr Pug	R					
Ling Pug	R	E				
Bleached Pug	R				N	
Pimpinel Pug					N	
Small Seraphim	R					
Peacock Moth	R					
Speckled Yellow	R					
Small Brindled Beauty	R					
Square Spot	R					
Brindled White-spot	R					
Grass Wave	R				N	
Maple Prominent	R					
Chocolate Tip	R					
Black Arches	R					

Red Data Book Moths (cont.)

	R Rarity	E Endangered	D Declining	B Red Data Book	N Nationally Notable	P Legally Protected
Round-winged Muslin	R	E				
Red-necked Footman	R	E			N	
Clouded Buff	R					
Light Feathered Rustic	R				N	
Lunar Yellow Underwing	R		D		N	
Square-spotted Clay					N	
Neglected Rustic	R	E				
White-marked	R				N	
Silvery Arches					N	
Glaucous Shears	R	E				
Northern Drab	R					
Striped Wainscot	R	E				
Southern Wainscot	R					
The Wormwood	R				N	
Golden-rod Brindle	R	E				
Sword Grass					N	
Pale-lemon Sallow	R				N	
Angle-striped Sallow					N	
White-spotted Pinion	R				N	
Reddish Light Arches	R					
The Concolorous	R	E		B		
Mere Wainscot		E			N	
Twin-spotted Wainscot	R					
Small Rufous	R	E				
Cream-bordered Green Pea	R				N	
Small Purple-barred	R	E				
Common Fan-foot			D		N	

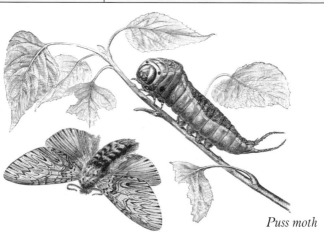

Puss moth

BEETLES

*T*he Red Data Book list of beetles is long, as might be expected for a group with 4000 representatives in Britain. The RDB gives details for 48 ground beetles, 57 water beetles and 237 other species. The beetles can be grouped into typical communities: woodlands, grasslands, disturbed sites, wetlands and specialised sites. Some beetles are found in designated sites such as SSSIs, where management can be specially tailored to their requirements; others, more evenly scattered throughout the countryside, are best conserved by promoting good land-use practices.

The woodland beetle community is particularly strong, especially in the ancient woodlands which form a link with the primeval forest cover of Britain. In natural woodlands, dead wood is far more common than it is in the managed woods that remain; many beetle species are critically dependent upon dead, often rotten, wood for shelter and feeding, and hence are very restricted in the places they are found. A rove beetle, *Ischnoglossa obscura*, has its only known British records in Leicestershire, in medieval

Rose chafer

deer parks, a habitat to which *Plectophloeus nitidus* and *Scraptia testacea* are also confined. *Sepedophilus bipunctatus* is found only in a pollarded willow at Narborough Bog. *Oxypoda recondita* is often associated with ants in mature trees. A bark beetle, *Kissophagus hederae*, is confined to dead ivy stems.

Ctesias serra is found under old dry loose bark on mature trees, especially pollards, and is associated with insect remains in spider webs. Adult *Ischnomera cyanea* beetles are often found on flowers, whilst their larvae develop in rotten wood. The removal of mature trees and dead wood poses a continuing threat even to the more widespread species. Some beetles are associated with living wood. The **musk beetle**, dependent upon willow species, has declined dramatically with the disappearance of osier beds. A leaf beetle, *Cryptocephalus querceti*, feeds on oak and is one of several species restricted to a few ancient pasture-woodlands, including Donington Park. Different species use the woodland ground layer, especially in damp woodlands with rotting vegetation and fungi, including two rare beetles, *Philonthus pseudoparcus* and *Atheta pilicornis*, the latter recorded on rotten stumps. Clear felling, drainage and conifer planting are threats to such species.

Grassland beetles face a different series of threats, principally the reduction in old grasslands as a result of agricultural intensification. The jewel beetle *Trachys scrobiculatus* is an example from lime-rich grassland, its larvae mining the leaves of ground ivy and related plants. An even more obvious example is the **glow-worm**, a specialist snail-feeder, requiring both open areas and tussocks for hibernation. Colonies of this species are scattered and in decline, so that records of females, glowing to attract males, are now a notable sight in Leicestershire and Rutland.

Damp meadows have disappeared as a result of agricultural improvement and drainage, bringing about declines in such species as the ground beetle *Carabus monilis*, the click beetle *Fleutiauxellus quadripustulatus* and the flea beetle *Longitarsus brunneus*, the last restricted to meadow-rue plants at Narborough Bog. The weevil *Grypus equiseti*, associated with horsetails, is now restricted to the Lount area (including a restored area of Lount Pit).

Disturbed sites of various sorts also support threatened communities of beetles. The glow-worm is again to be found in limestone quarries, with other species such as a ground beetle, *Harpulus obscurus*, a candidate for the national Red Data Book, found only at Geeston Quarry. Where the beetles of quarries are associated with particular plants – *Meligethes solidus* and rock-rose; the flea beetle *Phyllotreta aerea* on crucifers; a tortoise beetle *Cassida prasina* found on yarrow – they are vulnerable not only to obvious dangers such as landfill and insensitive restoration, but also to the invasion of scrub in abandoned sites. Another group is most commonly found in gravel pits. The ground beetle *Bembidion stephensi*, mainly a coastal species, is found on bare sand and clay by water. A water beetle, *Berosus luridus*, rare throughout Britain, is only recorded in a deep sandy pool in a disused quarry at Nevill Holt, whilst *Dryops similaris* is confined to the shallow cattle-trampled margins of Kilby Pit.

Heathland can be regarded as a naturally disturbed habitat, but one which has declined dramatically. Certain rare beetles are found in heathland: a rove beetle *Lamprinodes saginatus* is associated with ants; the brightly coloured *Selatosomus aeneus* is especially associated with scree slopes. The weevils *Stophosomus nebulosus* and *S. sus* feed on heather, and the predatory heather ladybird *Coccinella hieroglyphica* finds its home on that plant, so they are vulnerable to scrub invasion. Similarly, the **green tiger beetle** requires bare sandy areas where the larvae make burrows from which they prey on small animals, and the adults hunt by running over the ground; they suffer from growth of tall vegetation if grazing pressure is too light. Urban waste ground shares characteristics with heathland, and several heath species have recently come to light in urban Leicester, as has the coastal ground beetle *Amara convexiuscula*.

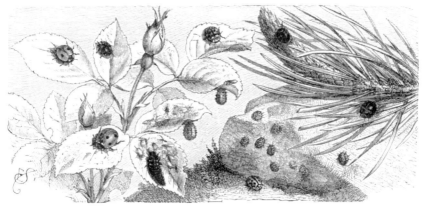

Ladybirds

Wetland habitats have declined over the years through drainage, pollution and neglect. Wetland beetles include not only the obvious aquatic water beetles, but also many species of generally terrestrial groups found on the margins of wetland habitats. Fens and carr (wet woodland) support, for example, the Dytiscid and Hydrophilid water beetles, as well as several species of ground and rove beetles. Of the former, *Blethisa multipunctata* is typical of marginal species which have declined in recent years, found only at Cropston Reservoir and Lockington Marsh.

58

Some wetland species will be naturally rare in the county – the water beetle *Helophorus flavipes* occurs amongst *Sphagnum* moss and rushes on the edge of acid pools, of which there are few, mainly in Charnwood. *Berosus signaticollis* is characteristic of shallow pools with wide fluctuations in water levels, and its only Midlands site is at Saddington Reservoir. *Atheta basicornis* is a wetland beetle found in rotten wood and under willow bark. The rove beetle *Oxypoda nigrocincta*, rare in Britain, has been found in a heavily shaded cut-off by the River Soar, where it will be vulnerable not only to drainage but also to infilling or deepening of river cut-offs.

The reed beetle *Donacia impressa* has larvae which develop in the roots of aquatic plants; its only local record is from a shallow well-vegetated pool by the River Eye. Another reed beetle, *Plateumaris affinis*, associated with sedges, has been found in a cut-off by the River Wreake; both these species would suffer from the clearing-out of ponds. Conversely, a few nationally rare beetles (such as *Helochares lividus*) are becoming more common as they are able to colonise newly-created ponds. A whirligig beetle, *Gyrinus aeratus*, of larger open water bodies is recorded only from the Grand Union canal.

Beetles of flowing water habitats are vulnerable to river management, but they may also be naturally tolerant of a certain degree of disturbance. The rove beetle *Bledius gallicus* is an example, found on the Soar where anglers had cleared the bank, but later lost to river engineering works. On the other hand, *Neobisnius villosus* is sensitive to trampling by grazing

Great diving beetle

animals. *Rhizophagus picipes* has been found amongst twigs in flood debris by the River Soar, and would be vulnerable to removal of trees from riverbanks. Species associated with tall marginal vegetation on rivers, such as the weevils *Notaris bimaculatus* and *N. scirpi* on the Soar, will be affected by management works involving removal of weed.

Another weevil, *Gymnetron villosus*, associated with water speedwells, has been found only on exposed sediment by the Soar at Barrow, which has been partly removed by river management works. Sediment of all sizes in rivers can be extremely important for its invertebrate life: the gravel beetle *Bembidion decorum* is recorded in Leicestershire only from a large shingle bank in the Trent. The whirligig beetle *Orectochilus villosus* is a nocturnal species of fast-flowing stony streams, spending the day under stones on the riverbank; it is threatened both by river works and changes in the adjacent land use. The River Lin is a particularly good example of a river supporting this type of fauna because it is little modified, another beetle present in it being *Ptenidium brenskei* – Bradgate Park is its only record in the whole of the East Midlands.

A restricted number of beetles form specialist communities, with strict habitat requirements and specific conservation needs. Several little-known species of the Leiodidae, associated with underground fungi, are found at North Luffenham Quarry. Other Leiodidae species are found in the underground homes of mammals – badgers and rabbits – whilst a rove beetle *Quedius puncticollis* is found in mole nests. Another rove beetle *Lamprinodes saginatus*, found at High Sharpley, is one of a small number of species associated with ant nests. In each case, conservation of the beetles will be dependent upon conservation of their hosts.

Dung beetles are of vital importance to recycling of nutrients in pasture. The dor beetle *Geotrupes vernalis* and the dung beetle *Aphodius zenkeri* are recorded only from deer dung in Bradgate Park. A few species are associated with dung heaps and other rotting vegetation – *Atomaria nigriventris*, a beetle formerly widespread in the countryside in haystacks, now has much reduced populations.

Red Data Book Beetles

Total number of species listed in each category:–	R Rarity	E Endangered	D Declining	B Red Data Book	N Nationally Notable	P Legally Protected
Ground Beetles	36	11	3	0	26	0
Water Beetles	38	10	1	4	42	0
Other Beetle Groups	190	24	7	31	169	0

OTHER INSECTS

*L*eicestershire and Rutland's dragonfly fauna runs to twenty-two species, of which sixteen are known to have bred. None of the country's rarest species have been recorded in the counties, but four of those which are present are notable on a national scale. The **ruddy darter**, formerly uncommon, has been increasing within the counties, through its ability to colonise newly created ponds. The **white-legged damselfly**, a dainty species which avoids polluted watercourses, has a notable population at the River Eye SSSI near Melton Mowbray, at the very north of its range in Britain, but has also been seen on some of the canals. The other two species are much less common in Leicestershire. The **variable blue damselfly** has only been recorded from three sites, notably the Grantham Canal. The few records for the **hairy dragonfly** are mainly in the early 1990s. Both species are rare in the Midlands generally, being found more frequently in coastal areas.

Dragonflies

The caddis flies are familiar as larvae in freshwater habitats, but the drab adults are less well known. Two Leicestershire species appear in the national Red Data Book. *Tinodes pallidulus* is only found in this county, in the Wood Brook and Burleigh Brook, having recently become extinct at its other known sites in Surrey, probably due to the effects of pollution. A similar threat faces *Hydropsyche saxonica*, another species of fast-flowing streams. As for the dragonflies, the maintenance and improvement of water quality standards in the counties' watercourses is essential for the survival of these species.

The true flies are the most numerous group of insects in Britain. Four Leicestershire species appear in the national Red Data Book, of which *Prionocera subserricornis*, a cranefly of fens, is given the highest category of threat, as "endangered". A snail-killing fly associated with aquatic snails, *Antichaeta analis*, is classed as "vulnerable", as is a soldier fly, *Oxycera analis*, found in springs and flushes. A hoverfly recorded from woodland rides, *Cheilosia nebulosa*, is categorised as "rare". In addition, there is a long list of flies found in Leicestershire and Rutland which are of national significance.

Left: Water stick insect; centre: Water boatman; right: Water scorpion

A nomad bee, **Nomada lathburiana**, is a nationally rare species, and several related species are nationally notable, including mining bees, ruby-tailed wasps, solitary wasps and a spider-hunting wasp, **Priocnemis schioedtei**. The **great yellow bumblebee** and **large garden bumblebee** may be species which need consideration in the two counties, but their status is uncertain.

Bumblebees

One plant bug, **Capsus wagneri**, is categorised as "rare" in the national Red Data Book; it is found in wetland habitats such as fens and canalside vegetation. Nationally notable species include a second plant bug, **Agnocoris reclairei**, found on willows in river valleys; a grassland plant hopper, **Agallia brachyptera**; and a lace bug, **Catoplatus fabricii**, dependent upon ox-eye daisies.

Like the dragonflies, none of Leicestershire and Rutland's grasshopper fauna is of national conservation concern. However, two species, the **mottled grasshopper**, inhabiting bare ground in heathy areas, and the **lesser marsh grasshopper**, found in rough grassland, are of local significance.

INVERTEBRATES

The native **whiteclawed crayfish**, the largest invertebrate found in Britain, lives in many of the smaller watercourses of Leicestershire, notably the Charnwood streams, as well as in the headwaters of the larger rivers and a few stillwater sites. The native freshwater crayfish population has suffered greatly in this country in recent years as a result of the introduction of non-native crayfish for farming. These alien species have brought in a disease, crayfish plague, which has devastated some populations of natives. Elsewhere, the alien species have established themselves in the wild and, being larger and more aggressive, have outcompeted the natives for food and habitat. Fortunately, as yet, crayfish plague has not occurred in Leicestershire, but American signal crayfish have established populations at a number of sites, notably in the Gaddesby Brook, where they are spreading and threatening the native crayfish of the River Eye SSSI. Control measures need to be implemented to halt the spread of the signals and eventually, if possible, eradicate them.

Woodlice, as crustaceans, are terrestrial relatives of the crayfish, but in their case there are several native species. Twenty-one species have been recorded in Leicestershire and Rutland and one of these, the pill woodlouse *Armadillidium pictum*, recently found at Buddon Wood, is the least common British species, categorised as "rare" in the national Red Data Book on invertebrates. Previously it has been found at a few rocky upland sites in the limestone mountains of northern England and in mid-Wales; in some ways, Buddon Wood (or what is left of it) can be regarded as an upland oakwood, not dissimilar to its other haunts. Another woodlouse, *Trichoniscoides* albidus, found in the soil in damp places, is a nationally scarce species.

Woodlice

Four Leicestershire spiders appear in the national Red Data Book for invertebrates. *Mastigusa macrophthalma* is rare in Britain, but has its stronghold in Charnwood Forest where it is found in ancient woodland, either in rotten wood or under large rocks and stones in peaty soil, usually in ant's nests. Its main threat is probably from roadstone quarrying, though most of its locations are SSSIs. Another ancient woodland species, *Centromerus cavernarum*, has only recently been discovered in Leicestershire, at Buddon Wood in 1996. *Lepthyphantes midas* is known from a colony inhabiting a single decaying ancient oak tree in Donington Park; its survival is dependent upon the continued existence of such old trees.

Water spiders

Rarest of all is *Lepthyphantes beckeri*, which is known in Britain only from a single female found amongst the ruins of Bradgate House in Bradgate Park. Only one other specimen of this spider is known to science, collected in a deer park in Berlin, and this may be Leicestershire's rarest animal! In addition to these four, 14 nationally notable spiders are found in Leicestershire. One of them, *Maso gallicus*, a relict wetland species found in Rutland, has been recorded in very few other counties.

Ramshorn snails

Related to the spiders, but much more rarely encountered, are the false scorpions, a group of small and harmless animals which live in crevices, particularly inside old rotting trees, under loose bark or in leaf litter. One national Red Data Book species, *Dendrochernes cyrneus*, has been recorded in Leicestershire from mature trees at Donington Park.

A nationally scarce freshwater snail, the **smooth ramshorn snail**, has been found at Lount Pit – an unexpected habitat which gives hope that it may turn up at other newly-created ponds around the county.

FLOWERING PLANTS AND FERNS

*T*he Red Data Book for flowering plants and ferns contains details of 136 species which are of conservation concern in Leicestershire and Rutland. These can be quite readily grouped according to the habitats that they occupy – wetlands, heathland, grasslands, woodlands and arable fields.

Wetland species form a high proportion of the total, reflecting the great extent to which wetland habitats have been lost to drainage, agricultural intensification, pollution and simply neglect. Amongst the plants of open water habitats, **floating water-plantain** is particularly significant, as it is highlighted in the European Habitats Directive as requiring special measures to protect its habitats; the only current record in Leicestershire, and the most south-eastern record in Britain, is at Beacon Hill. Several species of *Potamogeton* pondweeds, as well as **soft hornwort**, found growing underwater, have declined due to loss of ponds and dredging of canals. Loss and inappropriate management of ponds has also affected the attractive **water violet** and **frogbit**. River engineering works have been major factors in the decline of **fine-leaved** and **river water-dropworts**.

Plants which grow on the edge of open water include the only Leicestershire species to have appeared in the national Red Data Book on vascular plants; **thread rush**, found on stony lake shores, occurs at Blackbrook Reservoir, where scrub encroachment may be a problem. Ironically, some riverside trees and shrubs are themselves threatened. **Black poplar**, one of the rarest native British trees, is also rare in Leicestershire – it is known from only a handful of sites in the Soar Valley and North-West Leicestershire; the possibility of propagating it from cuttings is being considered. Similar rescue efforts might be attempted for **eared sallow**, a shrub of damp woodlands, only found as two specimens at Ulverscroft, a Wildlife Trust reserve.

Marshland and damp grassland habitats have declined enormously in the county, as demonstrated by the number of sedges which appear in the Red Data Book – eight in all, including two, **dioecious sedge** and **flea sedge**, now confined to single sites. Some of the most attractive marshland flowers are also much reduced in numbers and localities. This includes two of the orchids, **marsh helleborine** (only at Botcheston Bog) and **early marsh orchid** (rare at two or possibly three sites), as well as **bogbean** (one to three possible sites), **grass-of-Parnassus** (at Botcheston Bog only) and **marsh stitchwort** (two sites). Gravel extraction and inappropriate management (such as over-grazing) also threaten these sites.

Peatland habitats – wet heathland and bog – have now been almost entirely lost from Leicestershire and Rutland, and with them has gone a range of typical species. Land drainage has seen the decline of **bog pimpernel**, **common cottongrass**, and **black bog-rush** to very few sites. In the case of **cross-leaved heath** and **lesser skullcap**, the problem has been neglect of heathland management, leading to the spread of scrub and bracken. Even though dry heathland survives at several significant areas in Charnwood Forest, plants such as **petty whin** and

Grass-of-Parnassus

stag's-horn clubmoss still face the threats of fire and rock quarrying, and the clubmoss may now be extinct.

Despite Leicestershire formerly being noted for its grasslands, it is not only damp grassland which has been lost from the county – all types of grassland have disappeared to agricultural intensification. Fertilising, herbicide use and ploughing and reseeding all lead to the loss of sensitive grassland flowers such as the orchids – the **green-winged orchid**, especially characteristic of traditionally-managed hay meadows and neutral soils and once widespread, is now confined to eight sites, whilst the **frog orchid** is only certainly present at one and the **fragrant orchid** is also much reduced. **Dyer's greenweed**, once a source of yellow dye, and **little mouse-ear** have survived in part by adapting to life on railway verges. **Large thyme** is now only secure where it grows on and around Hallaton Castle, a scheduled ancient monument. The unusual fern **moonwort** has suffered not only from "improvement" of old grassland, but also lack of management and the spread of bracken.

Limestone is not very common in Leicestershire, so it is not surprising that a number of lime-loving plants are rare in the county, and many of them have probably never been common. The destruction of limestone grassland through agricultural improvement means that species such as **pyramidal orchid, basil thyme, carline thistle** and **yellow-wort** are now most frequently found in old quarries, where the threat is from scrub invasion. Some of the most attractive flowers are found on limestone, such as the **autumn gentian**, now reduced to six sites, and the spectacular **Pasque flower**, of which a small population clings on at one site in Rutland (though it may now be lost through accidental disruption of the site).

Woodland plants have generally fared rather better than those of more open habitats, and whilst there have been losses due to habitat destruction – the decline of **spreading bellflower** to a small population due to the quarrying of Buddon Wood, for example – the main threats have come from neglect and lack of management rather than direct destruction. **Wood vetch** and **nettle-leaved bellflower**, requiring open woodland, have declined with the demise of coppice management, as has **goldenrod**, though its current status is uncertain. **Purple small-reed**, favouring woodland rides, has suffered from scrubbing-over following neglect of the traditional management.

Carline thistle

One woodland shrub, **alder buckthorn**, is notably rare in Leicestershire, found at just a few sites in Charnwood Forest, at none of which are there more than two specimens; regeneration appears to be largely non-existent, competition from invasive rhododendron and sycamore possibly being a problem. The unusual chlorophyll-less **yellow bird's-nest**, which lives off decaying organic matter, was only discovered in Rutland comparatively recently, in 1964; it exists at one beech plantation at Ketton, where rather little is known about it. The **lemon-scented fern** is mainly found in woods, but also in damp shady places on heathland.

There is a group of plants which were once much more widespread in arable fields, often being seen as weeds, but now, due to agricultural intensification and particularly the widespread use of herbicides, are extremely rare. **Field gromwell** and **shepherd's needle** may already be extinct in Leicestershire, whilst **night-flowering catchfly, mousetail** and the **cornsalads** have been reduced to tiny populations. **Field mouse-ear,** ousted from the farmland, took to railway verges as an alternative habitat, but now suffers from scrub invasion on disused railway lines.

A small number of plants require rocky or bare habitats, so it is not surprising that they are rare in Leicestershire. **Green spleenwort**, for example, is found growing only on one blue brick bridge over the River Soar at Loughborough. **Brittle bladder-fern** is found on a similar site in Quorn as well as at the Abbey Pumping Station in Leicester. **Shepherd's cress** grows only on the slate quarry spoil mounds in Swithland Wood where it is threatened by birch scrub invasion. **Small** and **common cudweed** are both plants of bare places on sandy soils – quarries, waste ground and railway verges; little is known of them, and survey work is needed to determine their present status. **Danewort** is also found on waste ground and roadside verges, where there is little control over appropriate management – which probably includes a certain amount of deliberate disturbance.

The message for many of the Red Data Book plants is that appropriate management should help them to survive – but it should not be forgotten that even something as apparently common as bluebell has had to be given legal protection to ensure its future.

Danewort

Red Data Book Ferns

	R Rarity	E Endangered	D Declining	B Red Data Book	N Nationally Notable	P Legally Protected
Stag's-horn Clubmoss	R	E				
Rough Horsetail	R					
Wood Horsetail			D			
Moonwort	R	E				
Lemon-scented Fern			D			
Green Spleenwort	R					
Brittle Bladder-fern	R					

Red Data Book Flowering Plants

	R	E	D	B	N	P
	Rarity	Endangered	Declining	Red Data Book	Nationally Notable	Legally Protected
Pasque Flower	R	E			N	
Greater Spearwort			D			
Round-leaved Crowfoot			D			
Stream Water-crowfoot	R	E				
Hairy Buttercup		E	D			
Mousetail	R	E				
Soft Hornwort					N	
Field Pepperwort			D			
Smith's Pepperwort			D			
Shepherd's Cress	R					
Heath Dog-violet		E				
Marsh Violet			D			
Chalk Milkwort	R					
Night-flowering Catchfly		E	D			
Field Mouse-ear			D			
Dwarf Mouse-ear	R	E			N	
Little Mouse-ear			D			
Marsh Stitchwort	R	E				
Upright Chickweed			D			
Knotted Pearlwort	R					
Annual Knawel			D			
Alder Buckthorn	R	E				
Petty Whin	R					
Dyer's Greenweed			D			
Spotted Medick			D			
Slender Trefoil			D			
Sulphur Clover	R				N	
Subterraneum Clover	R					
Narrow-leaved Bird's-foot-trefoil		E	D			
Purple Milk-vetch	R	E				
Horseshoe Vetch			D			
Wood Vetch	R	E				
Grass Vetchling	R					
Hoary Cinquefoil	R	E				
Fragrant Agrimony	R	E				
Lady's Mantle		E	D			
Soft Downy-rose	R	E				
Navelwort	R					
Alternate-leaved Golden Saxifrage	R					
Grass-of-Parnassus	R					
Water Purslane			D			
Short-leaved Water-starwort	R				N	
Shepherd's-needle	R	E	D			
Lesser Marshwort	R	E				

Red Data Book Flowering Plants (cont.)

	R (Rarity)	E (Endangered)	D (Declining)	B (Red Data Book)	N (Nationally Notable)	P (Legally Protected)
Fine-leaved Water-dropwort	R	E				
River Water-dropwort	R	E			N	
Narrow-leaved Water-dropwort	R				N	
Common Bistort		E	D			
Small Water-pepper	R	E				
Marsh Dock	R				N	
Black Poplar	R	E				
Eared Sallow	R	E	D			
Creeping Willow	R					
Cross-leaved Heath			D			
Yellow Bird's-nest	R					
Water Violet	R	E				
Bog Pimpernel	R	E				
Brookweed	R	E				
Yellow-wort			D			
Autumn Gentian			D			
Bogbean	R	E				
Hound's-tongue			D			
Creeping Forget-me-not	R					
Field Gromwell	R	E				
Green Figwort					N	
Mudwort	R				N	
Common Cow-wheat			D			
Eye-bright (*Euphrasia anglica*)	R	E	D			
Eye-bright (*E. pseudokorneri*)	R	E			N	
Common Broomrape	R					
Large Thyme	R					
Basil Thyme			D			
Wild Clary	R					
Cat-mint	R	E				
Lesser Skullcap	R	E				
Buck's-horn Plantain	R	E				
Shoreweed	R					
Spreading Bellflower	R	E			N	
Nettle-leaved Bellflower			D			
Danewort			D			
Keel-fruited Cornsalad	R	E				
Narrow-fruited Cornsalad	R	E				
Small Teasel			D			
Small Cudweed			D			
Common Cudweed			D			
Heath Cudweed	R	E	D			
Goldenrod			D			
Carline Thistle			D			

Red Data Book Flowering Plants (cont.)

	R Rarity	E Endangered	D Declining	B Red Data Book	N Nationally Notable	P Legally Protected
Meadow Thistle			D			
Floating Water-plantain	R	E			N	
Frogbit	R	E			N	
Grass-wrack Pondweed					N	
Blunt-leaved Pondweed	R	E				
Bog Pondweed	R	E				
Hairlike Pondweed	R				N	
Opposite-leaved Pondweed			D			
Lily-of-the-valley	R					
Solomon's Seal	R					
Yellow Star-of-Bethlehem	R					
Thread Rush	R			B		
Marsh Helleborine	R	E				
Violet Helleborine			D			
Frog Orchid	R	E				
Fragrant Orchid	R					
Green-winged Orchid			D			
Early Marsh Orchid	R					
Pyramidal Orchid			D			
Greater Duckweed			D			
Common Cottongrass	R					
Needle Spike-rush					N	
Many-stalked Spike-rush	R	E				
Few-flowered Spike-rush	R	E				
Grey Club-rush	R	E				
Floating Club-rush	R	E				
Black Bog-rush	R	E				
Dioecious Sedge	R	E				
Star Sedge			D			
Tufted Sedge	R	E				
Tawny Sedge		E	D			
Smooth-stalked Sedge	R					
Flea Sedge	R	E				
Bottle Sedge	R	E				
Bladder Sedge	R	E				
Whorl-grass			D			
Fine-leaved Sheep's-fescue	R					
Mat-grass Fescue	R				N	
Narrow-leaved Meadow Grass	R					
Meadow Brome	R	E				
Purple Small-reed	R	E				

MOSSES AND LIVERWORTS

The lower plants are much less well known than the flowering plants, and only for the bryophytes – the mosses and liverworts – has a full Red Data Book been prepared for Leicestershire and Rutland. This identifies various threats to bryophytes, some of them common to other groups – drainage, loss of heathland and old grassland, removal of old trees – and others, such as air pollution and the reclamation of old quarries, being of particular concern for these plants.

Strangely, with the loss of heathland in Leicestershire, man-made habitats have become favoured by mosses and liverworts which were formerly living on heaths. Whilst species such as the moss *Pleurozium schreberi*, found in rocky clearings in heathland, has become very limited in the extent of its habitat, other species such as the liverwort *Gymnocolea inflata*, tolerant of pollutants, and the moss *Pogonatum urnigerum*, from wall tops and ditch sides, have found a home in old hard rock quarries. *Tortula amplexa*, a nationally scarce species, is found on bare clay in disturbed clay quarries; only female plants of this species are known, and it relies on vegetative regeneration from tubers for its reproduction. *Amblystegium varium*, normally by streams, ponds and on stones by lakes, is also known to be growing on wet sand beneath a conveyer belt!

Other species prefer old limestone quarries – *Soligera calcarea* requires the limestone to be exposed for several years before it can become established. *Pottia bryoides*, rare and found at only one site, is possibly under-recorded, not surprisingly as it is an annual plant of old limestone quarries which reaches its peak of development in the winter. *Bryum dunense*, a moss of dry lime-rich soils, has been identified around a cattle grid and in the grounds of a waterworks as well as on limestone quarry floors.

Another artificial habitat which is important for mosses and liverworts is that of churchyards, where walls, water collecting channels, gravestones and old trees all provide potential homes. Amongst the mosses found in such places are *Barbula convoluta*, on disturbed, nutrient-rich soil at the base of walls, and *Campylium chrysophyllum*, present not only on church walls and limestone outcrops but also on the terraced grass banks of a feudal castle bailey. Even derelict land can be significant for bryophytes: *Scleropodium cespitans* lives on soil, masonry and in grass amongst brambles on such sites, as well as on canal banks.

A wide variety of bryophytes can be found in woodland, with different species growing on different trees, and even variation between the trunks and branches of the same tree, determined by the availability of light and nutrients. Air pollution has affected many species, especially in more open woodland such as parkland, and whereas lichens, which were similarly affected, are now responding to better air quality, bryophytes do not seem to be recovering so quickly. *Dicranum montanum*, for example, living on the roots, trunks and branches of oak, birch and ash trees in woodland, appears to have declined due to acid rain, and the related *Dicranum tauricum*, which requires decaying wood and fallen timber, is also sensitive to high air pollution. On the other hand, *Orthotrichum affine*, growing on the trunks of elder, willow and ash, is more tolerant of air pollution than most other epiphytes (plants which grow on other plants).

Some woodland bryophytes are rather limited in their favoured habitat and hence, not surprisingly, are restricted in their distribution in Leicestershire and Rutland. *Bracythecium salebrosum*, requiring rotting wood in wet shaded woodland, is found on the roots of a beech at just one site. The liverwort *Metzgeria furcata* is a pioneer species on the middle part of ash, elder and poplar tree-trunks, and of necessity is tolerant of drought. *Fissidens exilis*, a winter ephemeral moss of neutral and acid soils in woodland ditches and rides, is threatened from shading out by leaf litter – the lack of management of many woodlands must be a problem here.

The mosses and liverworts are very much a damp-loving group of plants, so the loss of wetlands has hit them particularly hard. The *Sphagnum* bog-mosses, especially, inhabitants of wet heathland, have declined significantly and are now found only in Charnwood Forest, apart from occasional records in Rutland. Thirteen *Sphagnum* species appear in the Red Data Book. Typical of them is *Sphagnum squarrosum*, found amongst reedbeds, marshes and wet woodlands, often in the shade of other wetland plants, and also appearing in old wet acidic quarries; it is a species much threatened by drainage works. *Sphagnum fimbriatum*, growing amongst stagnant water upon rush tussocks in marshy woodland and old acidic quarries, is doubly threatened by drying out or by fast flowing water!

Chiloscyphus polyanthos, a liverwort which grows on the trees of alder and willow carr, is a species faced with loss of its habitat: there is very little carr (swamp woodland) left in Leicestershire. An aquatic liverwort, *Ricciocarpus natans*, which floats on the surface of base-rich pools or on damp mud, has been found in and on the banks of pools, lakes and canals, but a nationally scarce moss, *Ephemerum cohaerens*, a coloniser on the moist muddy bank of a Leicestershire reservoir, has not been seen in the county since its discovery in 1962. *Octodiceras fontanum*, an aquatic moss of canals, is apparently threatened by grazing by freshwater snails.

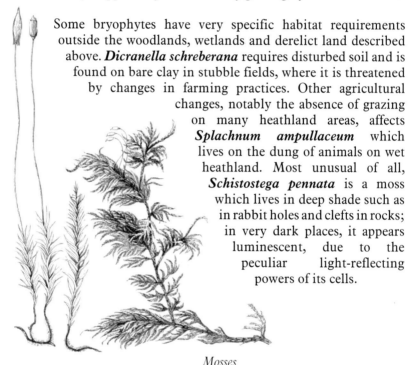

Some bryophytes have very specific habitat requirements outside the woodlands, wetlands and derelict land described above. *Dicranella schreberana* requires disturbed soil and is found on bare clay in stubble fields, where it is threatened by changes in farming practices. Other agricultural changes, notably the absence of grazing on many heathland areas, affects *Splachnum ampullaceum* which lives on the dung of animals on wet heathland. Most unusual of all, *Schistostega pennata* is a moss which lives in deep shade such as in rabbit holes and clefts in rocks; in very dark places, it appears luminescent, due to the peculiar light-reflecting powers of its cells.

Mosses

Red Data Book Mosses and Liverworts						
Total number of species listed in each category:–	R Rarity	E Endangered	D Declining	B Red Data Book	N Nationally Notable	P Legally Protected
Mosses	71	3	6	0	36	0
Liverworts	13	0	0	0	5	0

LOWER PLANTS

*A*lthough no Red Data Books have been published, draft red data lists have been drawn up for several other groups of the lower plants. Nearly 500 lichens are found in Leicestershire and Rutland, and a large number are rare or endangered in the counties, particularly those of ancient woodland/parkland and heathland. Two species – *Bacidia incompta*, dependent upon mature elms, and *Caloplaca virescens*, found on elm stumps in parkland – appear in the national lichens Red Data Book, being threatened by the decline in elm populations due to disease. Even where lichens do not face direct loss of their habitat, they are very sensitive to air pollution (indeed, lichens can be used as indicators of pollution levels). A number of ancient woodland rarities have survived in small numbers only because they have been sheltered from pollution by dense woodland: *Graphis scripta* and *Graphis elegans*, *Thelotrema lepadinum* and *Arthonia vinosa* are all relics of a lichen flora which was once common throughout lowland England before the Industrial Revolution.

Many threatened lichens reach the south-eastern limit of their British range in Leicestershire – for example, **rock tripe** and *Parmelia disjuncta*, growing on the hard old rocks of Charnwood Forest. *Haematomma ventosum* is particularly interesting as it is a mountain species surviving on rocks at the Charnwood Lodge nature reserve. Monitoring these species could be significant in assessing the effects of global warming. Other rock-dwelling lichens are restricted to churchyards, where they are threatened by over-enthusiastic management, especially cleaning of tombstones. *Caloplaca teicholyta*, at the northern edge of its range in Britain, is one of a number of species which have been found in a fertile form in Rutland churchyards.

A large number of fungi, exceeding 1200 species, are known from the counties, but it is difficult to say how rare individual species are. Fungi are present much of the time only as fine, almost invisible threads (hyphae) in the soil or in decaying vegetable matter. Their most visible parts, the fruiting bodies, are very erratic in their appearance, turning up in abundance in certain years but being absent for many years in between. For example, **death caps** were found many times in 1993, but seldom before or since. Another woodland gill fungus, *Volvariella bombycina*, was not recorded until 1996 when it suddenly appeared three times from widely separated areas.

Some fungi, though, are definitely known to be under threat. The bracket fungus **Rhodotus palmatus** has been brought to near-extinction by the decline in elm numbers – only a very few brackets can still be seen on old elm stumps. There is also an important group of fungi, notably the **waxcaps**, species of *Hygrophorus* and *Hygrocybe*, which live in old grassland and heathland, and have suffered from the loss of those habitats.

The algae of Leicestershire are even less known than other lower plants. The only groups to have been studied in detail are the desmids and diatoms, microscopic single-celled plants living in neutral and acidic waters. The greatest variety is to be found in the Charnwood area, but even here run-off from agricultural chemicals is raising the nutrient levels of the water. This affects certain sensitive species, which are disappearing, to be replaced by a more limited range of algae which are tolerant of nutrient-rich conditions. There is much scope here for further investigations, needing only the use of a high-power microscope to study these tiny but striking plants.

Fungi

THE FUTURE FOR WILDLIFE IN LEICESTERSHIRE AND RUTLAND

*A*s mentioned previously, several of the species detailed in this Red Data Book, and in the full volumes, are given protection by law. In addition, the habitats which they depend upon are protected in a number of nature reserves across the county – the Leicestershire and Rutland Wildlife Trust alone manages around 40 reserves, whilst others are run by local authorities and other conservation bodies. Yet this in itself will not secure the future of all the vulnerable species.

Much positive action for biodiversity conservation is now being stimulated thanks to the Biodiversity Action Plan initiative, which is leading to the drawing up of detailed action plans for the conservation of many key species and critical habitats. These plans may include bringing habitats back into appropriate management, re-creating habitats which have been lost, and possibly even re-introducing extinct species. The work at Rutland Water to encourage ospreys to nest in England again is just one such high-profile project.

Elsewhere, opportunities are being taken through initiatives such as the National Forest, which aims to transform the landscape of western Leicestershire, creating not only extensive woodlands but also other habitats such as heathlands and wetlands. The Loddington experimental farm, where trials are undertaken by the Allerton Trust to reconcile profitable farming with the preservation of wildlife interests, is pointing the way to measures which can be, and are being, taken elsewhere around the counties with the support of schemes such as Countryside Stewardship. If opportunities such as this are grasped, there is the real possibility of seeing more wildlife-friendly land use in the future, to the benefit of many Red Data Book species. Revised editions of the Red Data Book will provide a means of monitoring the success of this.

There are things that everyone can do to help with the conservation of the wildlife of Leicestershire, Leicester and Rutland. One is to give support to local conservation bodies. The Leicestershire and Rutland Wildlife

Trust is the principal organisation promoting wildlife conservation in the counties. It manages more nature reserves than all other bodies put together, and is always looking for practical assistance in carrying out that work, as well as general support for its activities. The Trust can be contacted at 1 West Street, Leicester LE1 6UU (telephone 0116-255-3904).

In order to conserve the area's wildlife, it is necessary to know as much about it as possible. Leicestershire Environmental Resources Centre, at Holly Hayes, 216 Birstall Road, Birstall, Leicester LE4 4DG (telephone 0116-267-1950), is pleased to receive records of animals and plants across the county, in order to help build up a comprehensive picture of the wealth of wildlife to be found here. Leicestershire Museums, Arts and Records Service, based at Holly Hayes, has run a number of surveys in recent years, looking for veteran trees, butterflies and rabbits and hares, for example, and new recorders are always welcome.

FURTHER READING

More information is available on some groups of animals and plants in Leicestershire and Rutland than others – and it is not necessarily the most obvious groups that are best catered for. The following references give more details on some of the species mentioned in this Red Data Book and in the full RDB volumes described on page 9.

Crocker, John and Daws, Jonathan (1996) *Spiders of Leicestershire and Rutland,* Loughborough Naturalists' Club/Kairos Press. A remarkably comprehensive work – the first ever county-wide spider fauna.

Grover, Steve, and Ikin, Helen (1994) *Leicestershire Dragonflies,* Leicestershire Museums, Arts and Records Service. An atlas and field guide to the counties' species.

Jeeves, Michael, Bullock, John, and Tobin, Robert (1994) *Nature Reserves in Leicestershire and Rutland: A Guide,* Leicestershire and Rutland Trust for Nature Conservation. Details of the reserves where many RDB species are to be found.

Messenger, Guy (1971) *Flora of Rutland,* Leicester Museums. An elderly, but useful, atlas of plant species in Rutland.

Primavesi, A L and Evans, P A (1988) *Flora of Leicestershire,* Leicestershire Museums, Arts and Records Service. A comprehensive atlas of plants, complementary to the Rutland volume.

Squires, Anthony and Jeeves, Michael (1994) *Leicestershire and Rutland Woodlands Past and Present,* Kairos Press. A fascinating account of woodland history and natural history, mentioning several RDB species.

Webster, Michael (1997) *Birds of Charnwood,* Kairos Press. A detailed account of Charnwood Forest birds including several rare species.

INDEX OF SPECIES